Comic Capers
THE DODGER'S DEN.
Teacher
HOME WORK
Swotty Simkins Homework
Maths and English

The Artful Roger

Mystery History

Published 2000 by BEANObooks geddes & grosset,
an imprint of Children's Leisure Products Limited,
David Dale House, New Lanark ML11 9DJ, Scotland



ISBN 1 84205 006 0

Printed and bound in Italy

CHAPTER ONE
The ARTFUL ROGER
THIS IS A HEARTBREAKING TALE OF POVERTY AND HUNGER AND GREED AND CRIME . . . IN FACT, ALL THE THINGS THAT MAKE FOR A GOOD FUN STORY! READ ON . . . IT'LL BRING TEARS TO A GLASS EYE! HA-HA!

OUR STORY BEGINS IN THE HAPPY HOME OF OUR ROGER, DODGER OF THE YEAR!
THAT WAS A LOVELY MEAL, MUM!
YES IT WAS . . .
. . . AND I'M DODGING THE WASHING-UP!
HERE A MINUTE, DOG! I NEED YOU, DEAR PET!
THIS DOG-UP-THE-JERSEY DODGE NEVER FAILS!
GRRRRR!
OH, DEAR! LISTEN TO MY STOMACH, PARENTS! IT'S UPSET! I MUST LIE DOWN!
I KNOW IT'S THE DOG . . .
. . . BUT I'LL DO THE WASHING-UP!
WE'LL DO EVERYTHING!
THIS IS THE LIFE! I'VE DODGERED THEM SO OFTEN, THEY'VE THROWN IN THE TOWEL!

LET'S SEE WHAT THE FILM'S LIKE, ROGER!
OH, YEEUK! A SOPPY ROMANCE!
AND AMERICAN FOOTBALL'S COMING UP ON THE OTHER CHANNEL! I'VE GOTTA ACT FAST!
I'VE SEEN THIS, DAD! HE'S REALLY A VAMPIRE — HE EATS HER UP THEN A CHAINSAW MANIAC ATTACKS HIM! IT'S RIVERS OF BLOOD! YOU WON'T LIKE IT! HONEST!
THAT'S A LIE — I KNOW YOU ONLY WANT AMERICAN FOOTBALL . . .
. . . JUST CHANGE THE CHANNEL! IT'S OKAY!
I MUST *REALLY* HAVE TIRED THEM OUT! THEY'LL DO ANYTHING I WANT!

BUT I BET THEY'LL STILL WANT ME IN BED BY HALF-PAST NINE!
THIS CALLS FOR A SUBTLE LATE DODGE!
HA-HA! THE VERY THING I'M LOOKING FOR!
Dodge 1249 B2 Staying up Late.
I THINK I'LL GO TO BED EARLY AND GIVE YOU BOTH SOME PEACE!
MY ROOM'S A BIT COLD, THOUGH, SO COULD YOU . . . SWITCH ON MY ELECTRIC BLANKET . . . FILL MY HOT WATER BOTTLE . . . WARM MY PYJAMAS AT THE FIRE . . . SEAL THE DRAUGHT UNDER MY DOOR . . . PUT ON AN EXTRA BLANKET . . .
NOW THEY'LL SAY . . . "OH, JUST STAY UP FOR A BIT!" YOU WATCH!
IT'S OKAY! WE KNOW IT'S DODGE 1249 B2, PAGE 81, STAYING UP LATE! BUT STAY UP IF YOU LIKE!

THINGS GET BETTER AND BETTER!
CHOCCIES! I MUST HAVE THOSE! I NEED DODGE NUMBER . . .
. . . 264 B MARK II, THE CHOC DODGE! DON'T BOTHER! JUST HAVE THEM ALL!
I GET THE FEELING ALL IS NOT WELL!
ENJOY YOURSELF . . . WHILE YOU CAN! DAD'S LOST HIS JOB, YOU SEE!
WHAAAT?
IT'S TRUE! AND WE MUST SELL THE HOUSE! WE'VE NO MONEY!
AND WE'VE HAD TO SELL THE FURNITURE TOO!
FOR SALE
FURNITURE

SO YOU SEE, WE'VE GOT LESS THAN NOTHING LEFT. GET THE PICTURE?
FURNITURE
WOW! THIS IS SERIOUS!
FURNITURE
BOOT!
OUT, DODGER! YOU'RE WORTHLESS!
THEY CAN'T DO THIS TO ME! I'M A BEANO SUPERSTAR!
PUT IN FOR A "DANDY" TRANSFER!

LET'S GO, ROGER!
TALK ABOUT SUDDEN! I DIDN'T EVEN CATCH THE END OF THE FOOTBALL!
WHERE *ARE* WE GOING TO LIVE, DAD?
OH, YOU'LL SOON SEE, SON!
IT'S NOT PERFECT, BUT IT'S HOME!
IT'S SURE NOT PERFECT I AGREE!
IT'S A BIT DRAUGHTY TO SAY THE LEAST!
PURRR!
YOU DON'T SO MUCH *PUT* THE CATS *OUT* IN THIS NEIGHBOURHOOD . . .

. . . AS TRY TO KEEP THEM OUT!
GOOD NIGHT, ROGER!
WHAT'S GOOD ABOUT IT?
VERY SOON—
AT LEAST IT'S QUIET!
ROAR! CLATTER! CLANG!
AAAGH! WHHASSAT NOISE??
LOOK! WE'RE LIVING IN THE MIDDLE OF THE MARKET!
FISH

CHAPTER TWO
FIGHTING BACK
I'VE HAD ENOUGH OF ALL THIS! WE ARE ON THE WAY BACK UP AGAIN!
LET ME HELP YOU UNLOAD, SIR!
THAT'S KIND OF YOU, YOUNG MAN!
AARGH!
THAT DIDN'T TAKE LONG! NOW YOU WON'T BE NEEDING THESE BOXES!
SUPRISE! SURPRISE! LOOK WHAT I'VE GOT!
OUR NEW HOUSE!

AND IF I CUT THROUGH HERE LIKE SO . . .
WE'VE ALSO GOT A ROOF! HOWZAT?
YOU'RE A GENIUS, ROGER!
WE CAN HAVE SOME NICE ROOF TILES!
NOW TO GET SOME BREAKFAST!
NO PEEKING NOW, READERS! I WON'T BE A MINUTE!
BLUSH!
RRIP! RRIP!
MEET THE PERFECT BEGGAR BOY — THE RAGGED ARTFUL ROGER! GOOD, EH?

TEAS 'N' GRUB
NO ONE WILL RESIST MY STARVING URCHIN ACT.
WAIL! IF ONLY I HAD A MORSEL FOR MY AILING MOTHER . . .
. . . AND POSSIBLY A CHEESEBURGER ROLL WITH DOUBLE PICKLE FOR MYSELF! WHINE!
HEE-HEE! FOOD COMING UP ANY MINUTE!
TEAS 'N' GRUB
BOP!
CLEAR ORF, FATSO!

STARVING INDEED! ME OWN KIDS ARE THINNER THAN YOU, TUBSO! NOW BEAT IT!
TIMES IS HARD!
ALL I GOT WAS AN EGG I CAN'T EAT!
YOU LOOK A LIKELY LAD! WHO ARE YOU?
I'M ROGER THE ARTFUL DODGER!
I COULD USE A GOOD DODGER! I'LL GIVE YOU A FREE MEAL!
I'M THE BEST DODGER IN THE BUSINESS!
NOW I NEED TO DODGE — AND FAST AT THAT!

ROLL UP! ROLL UP! HIT THE DODGER AN' YOU WIN A POUND!
SPLODGE!
LATER—
DO I GET MY MEAL NOW? A BOWL OF GRUEL PERHAPS?

YOU DIDN'T DODGE TOO WELL! YOU COST ME A FORTUNE!
STILL, I'M A MAN OF MY WORD! I PROMISED YOU FOOD!
GREAT! I'M STARVING!
'ERE! GO MAKE SOME SOUP!
YOU ROTTEN SWINDLER!
ROGER! WORRA NIFF! IT SMELLS LIKE CREAM OF OXEN'S ARMPITS!
ALL IT NEEDS IS A LITTLE PEPPER!
NO! DAD! DON'T DO THAT!
IT'S NOT FOR EATING!

IT'S FOR FILLING OUR HOTTIE BOTTLES!
GOOD IDEA, HUH? NOW WE'RE AS SNUG AS THE BUGS . . .
COSY
. . . AND THERE WON'T BE ANY PROBLEMS WITH ALLEYCATS TONIGHT!
NOT WITH THIS SOUPER MOGGY REPELLENT!

NOW FOR A GOOD NIGHT'S KIP AND TOMORROW WE'LL FIX MY BOSS!
TOMORROW —
WHERE IS THAT BOY? IT'S TIME HE STARTED HIS DODGING WORK!
I'M HERE AND I'M RETIRING TODAY!
WHAT?
AND TO BE FAIR I'VE DECIDED TO RETURN YOUR FOOD!
STINKER!
IF YOU DON'T WANT THIS I'LL ACCEPT IT!
TABLE AND SUN UMBRELLA NOW! WE'RE GETTING RATHER POSH — AND NOSH TOO!
WHAT A GOOD SON!

CHAPTER THREE
IN THE OLD NICK
NOW FOR THE ARTFUL ROGER GETTING EVEN MORE CASH!
HOW CAN I GET MONEY FAST?
THE ARTFUL DODGER SIMPLY NICKED THE READIES, BUT —
SNATCH
BUT NOTHING! YOU CAN NICK THE MONEY TOO!
IT'S MY BAD CONSCIENCE!
MAYBE HE'S RIGHT! TIME FOR CRIME!

THAT'S MY BOY! NICK THE OLD BIRD'S PURSE!
IT'S SO EASY!
THIS IS EASIER THAN WORKING FOR A LIVING!
NO! IT'S GOODY!
STOP, ROGER! THINK, MY BOY! DO NOT EMBARK ON A LIFE OF CRIME!
MY BETTER SELF!
DO NOT LISTEN TO YOUR BAD SELF! LET ME REMOVE HIM!
I KNOW YOU'RE A GOOD BOY AT HEART! YOU WON'T STEAL!
NO ONE PUSHES *ME* AROUND!
THINK! THINK!
WILL I BE BAD?
OR WILL I BE GOOD?

CHOKE ON YOUR HALO, GOODY!
YOU WON'T UPSET ME, BADDIE!
GOODY PEST!
BAD EGG!
STOP IT, YOU TWO! I NEED TIME TO THINK!
DO IT! DO IT!
DON'T! DON'T!
NO, I CAN'T STEAL! A BEANO BOY IS NEVER BAD!
RATS!
GOODY!
IN FACT I'LL WARN THIS POOR WOMAN ABOUT THE DANGERS OF LEAVING HER PURSE IN THE OPEN!
EXCUSE ME, MADAM.
WALLOP!
PICKPOCKET! WAA! I'M BEING MUGGED! HELP! POLEEEEECE!

THE LITTLE DEFENCELESS WOMAN ISN'T SAFE ANY LONGER! THAT THIEVING MONSTER! HE . . . HE . . .
CALM YOURSELF MADAM! HE'S NO THREAT NOW!
THANK YOU, CONSTABLE! YOU OBVIOUSLY KNOW THE TRUTH.
THE POLICEMAN SORTED THINGS OUT AND FIXED ME UP WITH A MEAL . . .
. . . PRISON FOOD! I'VE GOT SIX MONTHS IN THE NICK!

HA-HA! IT'S WHAT YOU GET FOR BEING GOOD!
SPLAT!
GET LOST, BADDIE! DO SOME PORRIDGE!
TWANG!
DINNER'S OVER! BACK TO YOUR CELL, ME OL' MATEY!
HOW DO I DODGE OUTA THIS LITTLE MESS?
DO NOT DESPAIR, GOOD ROGER! GOOD WILL ALWAYS OUT . . .
YOU CAN BE THE FIRST TO GET OUT, GOODY! OUT NOW!

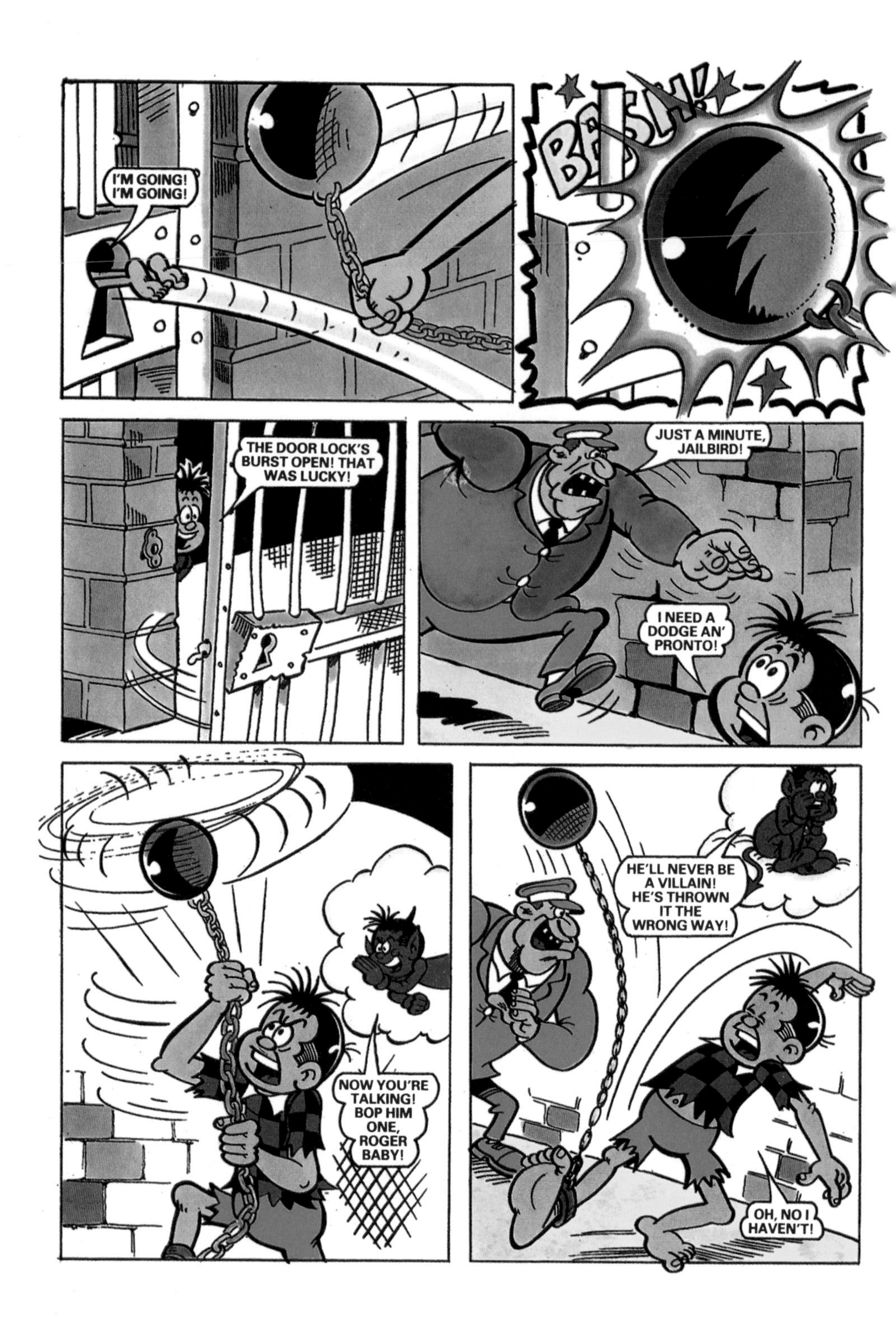
I'M GOING! I'M GOING!
BASH!
THE DOOR LOCK'S BURST OPEN! THAT WAS LUCKY!
JUST A MINUTE, JAILBIRD!
I NEED A DODGE AN' PRONTO!
NOW YOU'RE TALKING! BOP HIM ONE, ROGER BABY!
HE'LL NEVER BE A VILLAIN! HE'S THROWN IT THE WRONG WAY!
OH, NO I HAVEN'T!

OI! COME BACK
'ERE THIS MINUTE!
THIS IS THE
ONLY WAY
TO TRAVEL!
NOW TO GET RID
OF THIS BALL
AND CHAIN!

THIS COULD BE TRICKY! THERE'S NOTHING IN MY DODGE NOTEBOOK!
HOW CAN I CUT METAL?
CAN WE HELP?
IT'LL HELP IF YOU'LL BE FRIENDS AND SHAKE HANDS!
OH, WELL, IF YOU INSIST!
JUST WATCH THIS FIREWORKS DISPLAY, READERS!
THAT'S WHAT HAPPENS WHEN POSITIVE AND NEGATIVE FORCES COME INTO CONTACT!
ZIZ!
FLASH!
AND HERE COMES THE LITTLE FIREBALL!

THERE! IT'S CUT THE MANACLE CLEAN AS A WHISTLE!
ZAP
NOT A BAD DODGE, HUH?

CHAPTER FOUR
Buried Treasure
WHAT'S THIS, JOE? A NOTE FOR ME?
IT'S A TREASURE MAP! IT'S FROM OLD TOM WHO WAS IN THE CELL NEXT TO MINE.
TREASURE MAP
HE GAVE IT TO ME!
WE'RE GOING TO BE RICH!
THE TREASURE'S BURIED THIRTY-FIVE PACES NORTH OF THIS OLD OAK TREE.
BASH!
19, 20, 21, 22 . . .
Tisco's
OH, NO! OLD TOM'S BEEN IN JAIL SO LONG THEY'VE BUILT A SUPERMARKET ON TOP OF HIS TREASURE.
STILL, MUSTN'T GIVE UP TOO EASILY. LET'S THINK . . .

HARDWARE
I'LL NEED A FEW OF THESE TO DIG UP THE SUPERMARKET FLOOR . . .
PICKS
FORKS
. . . TWENTY-SIX, TWENTY-SEVEN, TWENTY-EIGHT, TWENTY-NINE . .
GAH! THE TREASURE'S DIRECTLY UNDER ALL THOSE SOAP PACKETS.
SOAPO
HOW TO GET RID OF THE SOAP POWDER . . . ?
DODGE BOOK 11
LADIES! WATCH THIS CLOSELY. NOT ONLY DOES 'SOAPO' GET THIS SHIRT CLEANER THAN OTHER POWDERS . . .

. . . IT MAKES THE SHIRT AS GOOD AS NEW! YOU DON'T BELIEVE IT?
SOAPO
LOOK! IT'S BETTER THAN NEW. IT'S BACK IN ITS PACKET AND IT'S WHITE!
£10
THAT IS FANTASTIC!
THAT IS ANOTHER SHIRT! BUT THEY DON'T KNOW — AND 'SOAPO' IS DIS-APPEARING FAST!
SOAPO
JUST THINK! THE TREASURE'S ALMOST IN MY HANDS.
DIZ
AAAGH! MORE SOAP POWDER!
I DON'T KNOW WHO YOU ARE, BUT KEEP UP THE SALES TALK. I'M SELLING HUNDREDS OF PACKETS. HERE'S A SMALL TIP.
£10

IT'S HARDLY A FORTUNE, BUT IT'S A START.
HOWEVER, I'VE GOT TO GET RID OF ANOTHER BATCH OF SOAP POWDER.
DIZ
SOON —
THIS *NEW* POWDER IS EVEN BETTER THAN SOAPO. WATCH CLOSELY!
IT'S SO POWERFUL, IT JUST EATS DIRT AND STAINS . . .
DIZ
SHOCK
. . . AND MELTS YOUR ARMS IF YOU TOUCH IT!
HORROR
MY HANDS! I'M FINISHED. I'LL NEVER BE ABLE TO PLAY PIANO AT THE ORPHANAGE AGAIN!
THEY'RE FALSE PLASTER ARMS! GOOD DODGE, EH? NOW, EXCUSE ME . . . MORE ACTING'S NEEDED HERE.

POOR BOY! WAAA!
SOB!
BOO-HOO!
I'M AN ORPHAN! WHO'LL HOLD MY BEGGING BOWL NOW? I'M DOOMED! SOB! DOOMED!
IT'S DREADFUL! HOWL!
DIZ
DIZ
FIZZLE BUBBLE!
SMART, HUH? ALL THIS WEEPING IS TURNING THE POWDER INTO LOTSA SUDS.
THAT'S FIXED THE SOAP POWDER!
NOW I CAN DIG BEHIND THE SOAPY SMOKESCREEN.
TREASURE HERE I COME!
IT'S TRUE! IT'S OLD TOM'S FORTUNE. I WONDER HOW MUCH IS IN IT?

BACK IN PRISON —
VISITING ROOM
WELL, YOU SEE, ROGER, FOUR POUNDS, SEVENTEEN SHILLINGS AND FOURPENCE *WAS* A FORTUNE WHEN I WAS LOCKED UP IN 1902!
CARDBOARD CITY
MONEY! AT LAST! HOW MUCH DID YOU GET, ROGER?
NOT A LOT!
GIMME THAT, ROGER!
TAKE IT EASY, DAD!
A PENNY! AN *OLD* PENNY! AND IT'S ALL MINE!
DAD'S CRACKERS! IT'S THE STRAIN!
IT'S A VERY OLD PENNY! A VERY, VERY, VERY NICE OLD PENNY!
TAKE IT EASY, DAD! I'LL GET YOU A NEW ONE IN A MINUTE!

NO, YOU DON'T UNDERSTAND! IT'S THE ONLY ONE OF ITS KIND. IT'S VALUABLE! WE'RE RICH!
WELL, THAT'S THE BEST NEWS I'VE HEARD THIS WEEK!
OH, WE'RE RICH, WE'RE RICH, WE'RE RICH, WE'RE RICH, WE'RE RICH!
LATER —
HAVING A HARD TIME SINCE I BOOTED YOU OUT, OLD BOY! HA-HA! NOTHING PERSONAL, YOU KNOW. I'M ALL RIGHT!
DAD'S OLD BOSS
PING!
HERE'S A PENNY, OLD BEAN! EVERY PENNY HELPS! HAW! HAW!
OH, WE KNOW ALL ABOUT PENNIES, SIR!
CATCH!

VROOM!
OURS WAS WORTH A PRETTY PENNY! 'BYEEE!
HAVE A DRINK ON US, BALDY!
VROOOM!!
I HATE BEING CALLED BALDY IN FRONT OF YOU, DEAREST.
I WOULDN'T WORRY ABOUT IT, SHWEETIE!
HI, DIDDLY-DEE, A DODGER'S LIFE FOR ME!
THE END

CHAPTER ONE
"MYSTERY HISTORY . . ."
IT'S HISTORY PERIOD IN CLASS TODAY! JUST WATCH HOW I AVOID THE UNPLEASANT EXPERIENCE!
TODAY WE WILL DISCUSS THE WARS OF THE ROSES . . .
A PRICKLY SUBJECT INDEED!
ANY QUESTIONS ON WHAT WE DISCUSSED LAST WEEK?
WHAT DID THE BLACK PRINCE SAY TO LORD DODGERWORTH ON THE EVE OF THE BATTLE OF AGINCOURT?

"LEAVE MY SIDE AT ONCE, ROGER!"
RIGHTO! I NEVER DISOBEY THE WORDS OF THE TEACHER! I'M OFF.
BACK HOME —
GO ROUND TO GRANDAD'S AND HELP TIDY UP HIS OLD BOOKS!
SOUNDS LIKE HARD WORK!
PACK ALL THESE OLD BOOKS INTO BOXES AND STORE THEM IN THE ATTIC!
A SWIFT DODGE NEEDED HERE, READERS!
COO! LOOK AT THIS! DODGE BOOKS FROM ANCIENT TIMES! GRANDAD MUST HAVE COLLECTED THEM!
PUFF!
COUGH!
CLAN OF THE CAVE DODGER
I WONDER IF I CAN PICK UP ANY DODGES FROM THE CAVEMAN TIMES? . . .
"IN THE BEGINNING OF TIME, THERE LIVED A CAVE-BOY BY THE NAME OF ROJAHH . . ."

". . . HE LIVED IN A NEANDERTHAL DWELLING WITH HIS DAD BAH-REE. ROJAHH WAS A VERY UNHAPPY CHAPPIE . . ."
WELL NOT *ALL* THE TIME! SOMETIMES I'M QUITE GOOD COMPANY!
TROUBLE IS,THERE'S NOT MUCH GOING ON ROUND HERE! NO-ONE'S INVENTED ANYTHING YET!
NO VIDEOS! NO TELLY! NO DISCOS!
THE ONLY TREAT IS A BOWL OF COLD PORRIDGE! NO WONDER I'M UNHAPPY! YEUK!
SLURP!
IF THINGS ARE REALLY GOOD I GET RAW DINOSAUR DRUMSTICKS FROM MAAHKDONALDS!
WIERDORAMA!
AS WE'VE NO TELLY WE JUST WATCH THESE CAVE PAINTINGS!

LATER —
IT'LL SOON BE MEALTIME — BUT OUR STORE CUPBOARD IS BARE!
YUMMY! FRESH FOOD! A PLUMP, JUICY BABY DINOSAURUS!
WATCH ME FELL IT WITH ONE CLEAN BLOW TO THE DINOSAURUS BONCE . . .
BAH! MISSED!
HEE! I'M OFF THE MENU!
LOOK AT THOSE SHINY LIGHTS! I'LL CALL THEM SPARKS!
CHUNK
IT'S COSY TOO! NICE!
WELL, WHAT DO YOU KNOW! I'VE INVENTED FIRE!

GRAAH!
YIKES! HERE COMES TROUBLE! THE BABY DONOSAURUS'S DAD!
IT'S MY MUMMY ACTUALLY! DAD'S TOO BIG FOR THIS PAGE!
I'LL HIDE BEHIND THIS LOG 'TIL IT GOES AWAY!

GREAT STONE-AGE STINKERS! ROUND LOGS ROLL!
I THINK I'VE INVENTED THE WHEEL AS WELL!
NNNGH! TOO BAD I'VE ALSO INVENTED THE EMERGENCY STOP!
DONK!
OOYAH!
HAH! WHAT A DAY! I'VE DISCOVERED HOW TO GET MILK OUT OF COCONUTS — AND INVENTED THE MUG!
I MUST WRITE DOWN HOW I WANGLED ALL THESE INVENTIONS . . .
. . . AND SO ROJAHH INVENTED THE VERY FIRST *DODGE BOOK VOLUME ONE!*

WELL, WELL! FANCY THAT! HOW INTERESTING!
I WONDER WHAT THIS NEXT BOOK'S ALL ABOUT?
The Rise Fall of the Rojan Empire
LISTEN CAREFULLY NOW AND I'LL READ IT TO YOU! IT'S ALL ABOUT THE RISE AND FALL OF THE ROJAN EMPIRE!
"IN THE DAYS OF THE ROJAN EMPIRE LIVED ROGERIUS A SIMPLE SLAVE BOY . . ."
WHAT A LIFE — SLAVING AWAY IN THE SERVICE OF THE MAD EMPEROR BARRIGULA!
I'M GOING TO MAKE MY HORSE A SENATOR!
HE'S TOTALLY BONKERS!
AND THAT'S THE MOST SENSIBLE THING HE'S SAID FOR AGES!
MIND YOU, THE HORSE HAS PROBABLY GOT MORE BRAINS THAN THE DODDERING OLD FOSSILS WHO *ARE* SENATORS!

CLEANSE THE STABLES WITH THIS GOLDEN SPOON OR YOU'RE ON THE LIONS' MENU TONIGHT!
HOW CAN I REFUSE?
AND DON'T FORGET TO REFILL THE HORSE TROUGH!
BY THE STARS! WHAT A SMELL! I'LL NEED THE GOLDEN CLOTHES PEG FOR THE NOSE!
IT'LL TAKE TILL THE IDES OF MARCH TO MUCK OUT WITH THIS SPOON!
MUSTN'T FORGET TO REFILL THE HORSE TROUGH OR BARRIGULA WILL FLIP!
IT'S SO PEACEFUL IN HERE . . . QUIET . . . THE RIPPLING OF . . . THE . . . WATER . . .
MORE GRAPES LORD ROGERIUS?
YOUR COLA, SIRE!
"AND SO ROGERIUS DRIFTED OFF TO SLEEP . . . AND IN HIS DREAM HE DALLIED IN BARRIGULA'S BATH WITH THE EMPEROR'S FAIR MAIDENS . . ."
GOOD DREAM! SURE BEATS STABLE CLEANING!

KISS ME, VOLUMINA!
AT ONCE, SIRE!
AAAGH! WHASSAT? THE STABLE DOG'S LICKING MY CHOPS!
SLURP!
WAKEY! WAKEY!
AND THE STABLES ARE FLOODED! BARRIGULA WILL BE FURIOUS!
BUT WAIT — THE FLOOD WATERS ARE WASHING OUT THE STABLES! THE PLACE IS SPOTLESS! WHEEE!
AMAZING! IT'S SO CLEAN I COULD EAT OFF THE FLOOR! IN FACT I WILL!
GREAT DODGE!
. . . AND WITH ALL THE SCRAPS IN THE DOGIUS BAG, THE SLAVES WILL DINE WELL TONIGHT! WHAT A DAY!
DOGIUS BAG

CHAPTER TWO "SLAVE OF THE FAT QUEEN"
I WONDER WHAT'S NEXT? THIS LOOKS LIKE AN OLD SCROLL! . . .
ZZZ
PUFF!
WELL, WELL, WELL! FOUR WELLS IN FACT! IT'S THE DODGE SEA SCROLLS . . .
THE DODGE SEA SCROLLS
HMMM! IT'S ALL UNREADABLE! IT'S THOSE HIEROGLYPHIC THINGIES . . . SYMBOLS INSTEAD OF WORDS . . .
?
JUST AS WELL GRANDAD HAS AN ENGLISH-EGYPTIAN DICTIONARY!
EGYPTO-ENGLISH DICTIONARY
IN THE LAND OF THE PHARAOHS LIVED A MISCHIEVOUS PRINCE — TUTANROJAN! . . .
THAT'S ME! HOW DO, FOLKS!

"TUTANROJAN WAS THE BROTHER OF QUEEN CLEOFATRA, WHO ATE SEVERAL CAMEL PIES EVERY DAY . . ."
YOU JUST CAN'T BEAT THE FEELING!
CAMEL PIE
I'LL WASH DOWN LUNCH WITH A BATH OF ASSES' MILK! SLOORP!
I AM BASHAN, THE DONKEY MILKER — AND BASHAN RESIGNS!! END OF MY PART IN THE STORY!
TUTANROJAN! YOU'LL HAVE TO TAKE OVER! *YOU* MILK THE ASSES! I NEED TO BATHE IN ASSES'MILK SHORTLY!
OH, BRILL! THANKS A BUNCH!
AND SO —
NICE DONKEYS! GOOD DONKEYS! MILKING TIME — TURN THE UDDER CHEEK!
NOT AGAIN!

THUD! SNORT! BOOT! BRAY!
"AND SO TUTANROJAN LEARNED A VALUABLE LESSON — NEVER MILK DONKEYS — ESPECIALLY WITH COLD FINGERS!!"
AAAGH!
I FEEL AN ASS — BUT ALL IS NOT LOST!
NO PEEKIN' NOW! QUEEN CLEO'S STARKERS!
GERONIMO! ASSES' MILK HERE I COME . . .
WHO SWAPPED ASSES' MILK FOR WHITEWASH??!!
WHO INDEED! TIME FOR A SHARP EXIT!

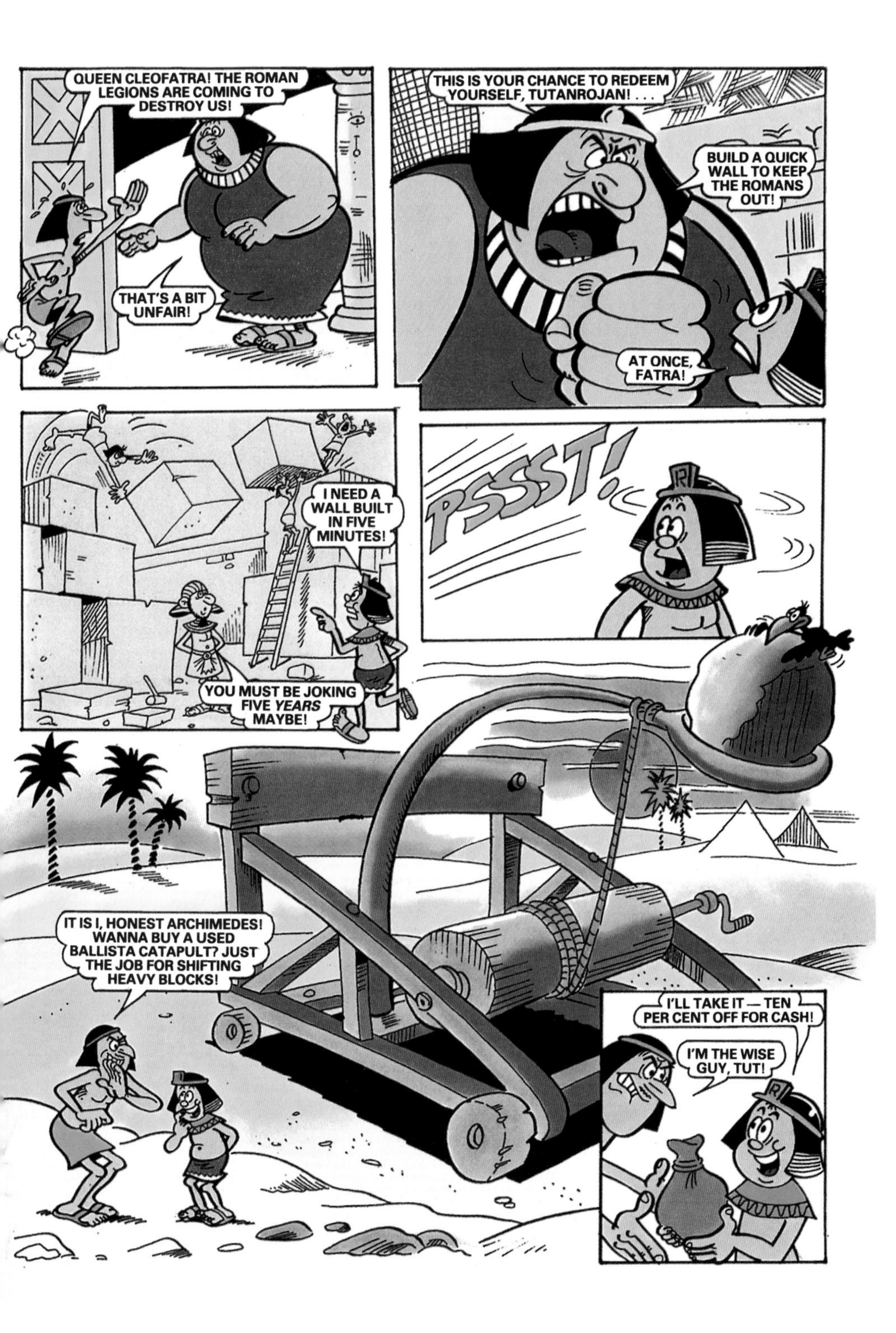
QUEEN CLEOFATRA! THE ROMAN LEGIONS ARE COMING TO DESTROY US!
THAT'S A BIT UNFAIR!
THIS IS YOUR CHANCE TO REDEEM YOURSELF, TUTANROJAN! . . .
BUILD A QUICK WALL TO KEEP THE ROMANS OUT!
AT ONCE, FATRA!
I NEED A WALL BUILT IN FIVE MINUTES!
YOU MUST BE JOKING FIVE *YEARS* MAYBE!
PSSST!
IT IS I, HONEST ARCHIMEDES! WANNA BUY A USED BALLISTA CATAPULT? JUST THE JOB FOR SHIFTING HEAVY BLOCKS!
I'LL TAKE IT — TEN PER CENT OFF FOR CASH!
I'M THE WISE GUY, TUT!

BOING! BOING!
THIS IS WALL-BUILDING MADE EASY!
— BUT USELESS AT BUILDING WALLS!
BOING!
YOU'VE GOT TO HAND IT TO THESE EGYPTIANS — THEY'RE GREAT AT BUILDING PYRAMIDS!
YOU USELESS SCARAB! I'LL HAVE YOU THROWN INTO A PIT OF ASPS! LIKE THAT?
ASP ME ANOTHER!
APPEARING TONIGHT SANDY SANDI AND SANDEE THE SAND SOUND
I'VE GOT TO MAKE MYSELF SCARCE — BEFORE I'M EXTINCT!
WHERE IS THAT LITTLE SON-OF-A-CAMEL! I CAN'T SEE HIM ANYWHERE!

EROOPS! CAN'T SEE WHERE I'M GOING!
SO! THERE YOU ARE! YOU CAN'T HIDE BEHIND THAT DISHCLOTH FOR EVER! NOW I'LL HAVE YOU TORN LIMB FROM LIMB!
PREPARE TO MEET THY DOOM! SOON YOUR WORTHLESS INSIDE BITTIES WILL BE SPILLED ON THE SANDS OF TIME!
I GUESS THIS MEANS SHE DOESN'T LIKE ME! YOU RECKON?
HOW WILL HE DODGE OUT OF THIS CAMELS' MESS?
OH, HE'LL FIND A WAY! JUST YOU WATCH!

NOW, HOW DOES THAT TUNE GO? THE ONE THE SAND DANCERS WERE SINGING? . . .
WHAT'S THIS? SINGING?
HE'S PLAYING OUR TUNE! LET'S DANCE . .
AARGH! WHAT'S THIS? HE'S CHARMING THE HUMPS OFF MY CAMELS!
DA-DA-DA-DI-DI-DA . . . SLOW, SLOW, QUICK, QUICK, SLOW . . . DA, DOO, DA, DI, DA, DI, DA . . . SLOW, SLOW . . .
PLAY IT AGAIN, SAM! . . .
QUICK, QUICK, QUICK, QUICK, QUICK . . .
KEEP ON TRUCKIN'!
BYE-EE, FATRA! SEE YA!
COME BACK! YOU CAN'T JUST DANCE AWAY LIKE THAT — IT'S A LADIES' CHOICE, YOU WRETCH!

CHAPTER THREE
"ROGNAAR THE BARBARIAN"

AAH, I LIKE THOSE OLD EGYPTIAN STORIES! THEY DON'T WRITE THEM LIKE THAT ANYMORE! NOW, WHAT'S NEXT IN GRANDAD'S PILE OF BOOKS . . .
THIS LOOKS GOOD, JOE! "THE LEGEND OF THE VIKINGS" . . . WHAT'S THIS ALL ABOUT?
THE LEGEND OF THE VIKINGS
KOFF!
LONG AGO IN THE NORWEGIAN FIORDS LIVED A YOUNG VIKING LAD NAMED ROGNAAR . . .
HERE COME THE WAR LONGBOATS, ROGNAAR! SOUND THE CLARION CALL . . .
AT ONCE, FATHER!
NOW, A DEEP, DEEP BREATH AND I'M ALL SET . . .

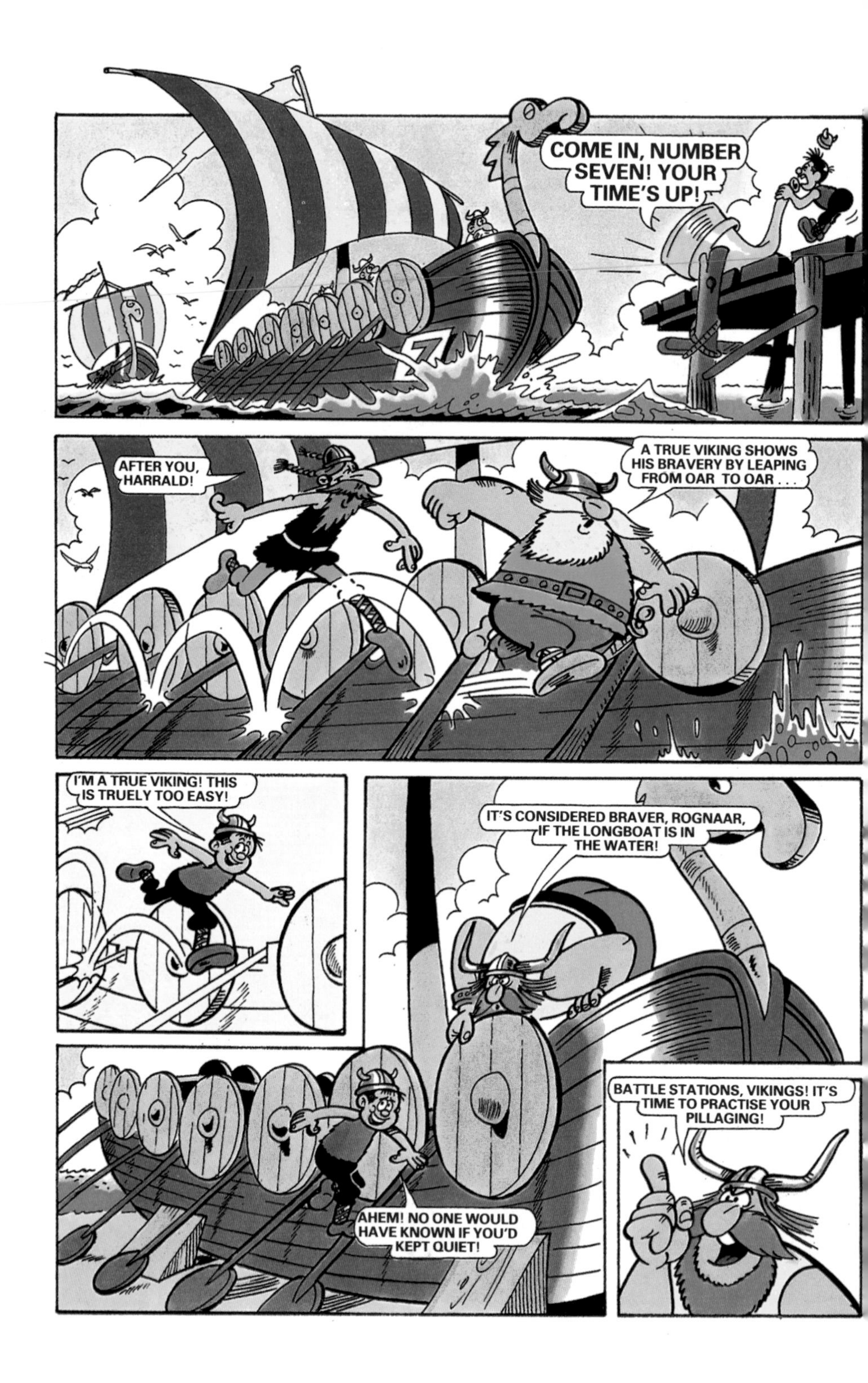
COME IN, NUMBER SEVEN! YOUR TIME'S UP!
AFTER YOU, HARRALD!
A TRUE VIKING SHOWS HIS BRAVERY BY LEAPING FROM OAR TO OAR . . .
I'M A TRUE VIKING! THIS IS TRUELY TOO EASY!
IT'S CONSIDERED BRAVER, ROGNAAR, IF THE LONGBOAT IS IN THE WATER!
AHEM! NO ONE WOULD HAVE KNOWN IF YOU'D KEPT QUIET!
BATTLE STATIONS, VIKINGS! IT'S TIME TO PRACTISE YOUR PILLAGING!

GET CRACKING, ROGNAAR! RUSH UP AND BASH THAT DUMMY PEASANT ON THE HEAD THEN PILLAGE HIS VILLAGE!
PILLAGE HIS VILLAGE? THIS SOUNDS TOO DANGEROUS!
I FEEL A DODGE COMING ON, FOLKS . . .
FIRST, I'LL JUST WAGGLE THE EARS OF MY HELMET . . .
. . . AND OH, DEAR, OH, DEAR . . . IT JUST FLIES AWAY!
SORRY, DAD! I CAN'T DO ANY PILLAGING WITHOUT MY SAFETY HELMET!
IS THAT SO, MY SON?
NOT TO WORRY . . . I HAVE LOTS OF SPARE HELMETS HERE!
I WAS AFRAID YOU'D SAY THAT, HARRALD-DAD!

BUT THIS ONE'S TOO SMALL . . .
. . . AND THIS ONE HAS THE HORNS ON BACK TO FRONT!
AND *THIS* ONE HAS THE HORNS ON UPSIDE-DOWN!
TOOOT!!
THIS HAS MOTOR HORNS TO WARN OF APPROACHING PILLAGERS! THAT'S NO GOOD!

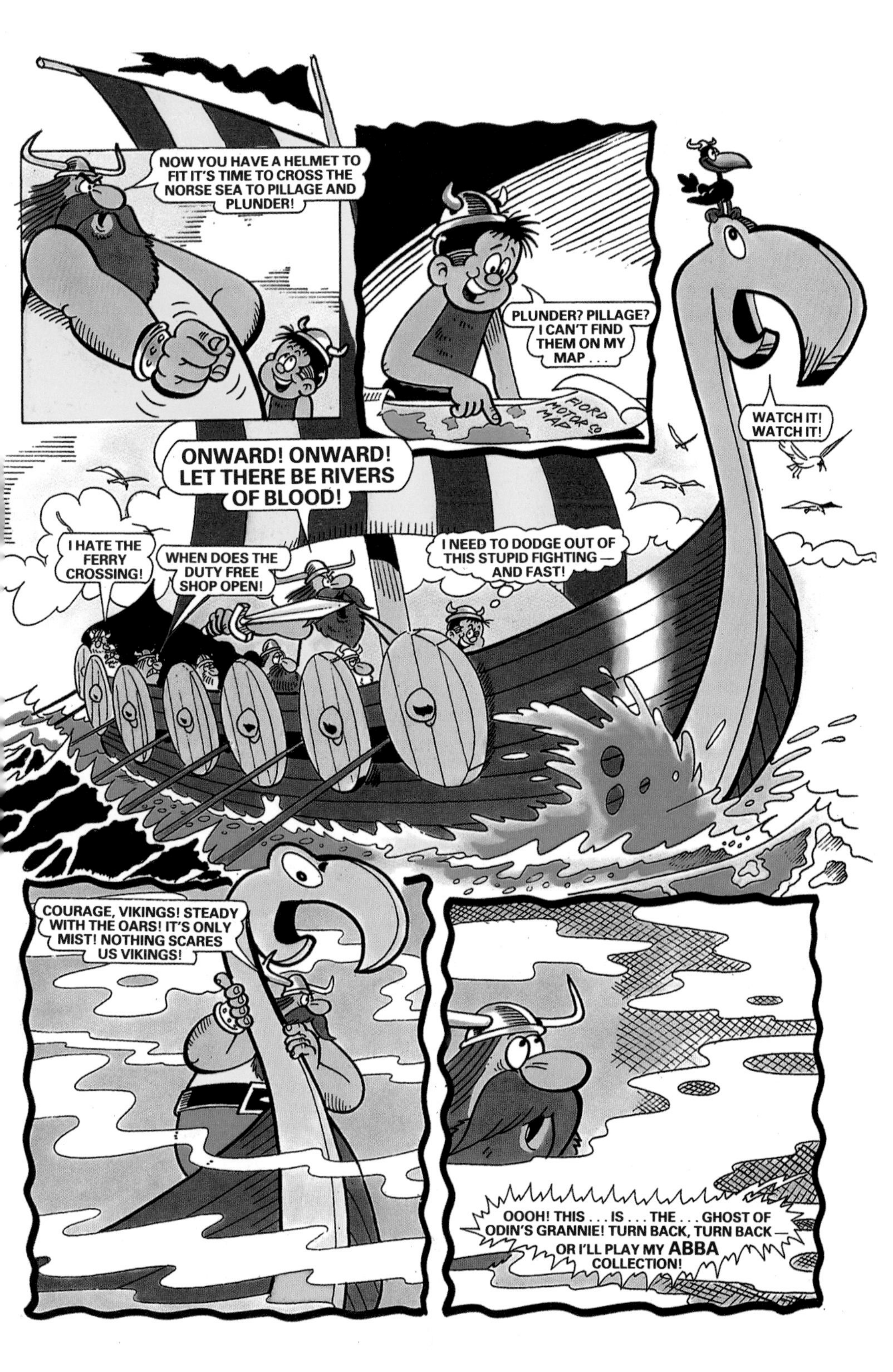
NOW YOU HAVE A HELMET TO FIT IT'S TIME TO CROSS THE NORSE SEA TO PILLAGE AND PLUNDER!
PLUNDER? PILLAGE? I CAN'T FIND THEM ON MY MAP . . .
FIORD MOTORS MAP
WATCH IT! WATCH IT!
ONWARD! ONWARD! LET THERE BE RIVERS OF BLOOD!
I HATE THE FERRY CROSSING!
WHEN DOES THE DUTY FREE SHOP OPEN!
I NEED TO DODGE OUT OF THIS STUPID FIGHTING — AND FAST!
COURAGE, VIKINGS! STEADY WITH THE OARS! IT'S ONLY MIST! NOTHING SCARES US VIKINGS!
OOOH! THIS . . . IS . . . THE . . . GHOST OF ODIN'S GRANNIE! TURN BACK, TURN BACK — OR I'LL PLAY MY ABBA COLLECTION!

NOW THAT REALLY IS SCARY!
GO HOME, VIKINGS! TURN NOW IN TIME TO SEE REPEATS OF THE "ODIN LINE" ON TELLY!
HAVING FUN, ROGNAAR?
OH, HELLO, DAD! JUST A LITTLE JOKE!
GAH! VIKINGS HAVE NO SENSE OF FUN! I'M POSTED AS LOOKOUT AS A PUNISHMENT!
LAND AHOY!
GAH! YOU'RE A BIT LATE WITH YOUR CALL, ROGNAAR!

THE TIME OF KILLING AND LOOTING AND PILLAGING HAS COME! LET MIGHTY THOR GUIDE OUR BATTLE-AXES — LET THEM SING THE *SONG OF DEATH!!*
I DON'T LIKE THE TUNE HE'S CALLING AT ALL, AT ALL!
. . . ER . . . UM . . . HOW'S ABOUT A QUICK CHORUS OF *ODIN THE RED-NOSED REINDEER* AND HOME FOR TEA? YES . . . NO?
VIKING SONGS
FOOLISH YOUTH! WOULD YOU WISH TO BRING SHAME ON YOUR FIORD HOME?
. . . WELL, IT *DID* OCCUR TO ME AS A POSSIBLY GOOD IDEA, YES!
CHOP!

COME, LET US PUT THEIR PUNY MENFOLK TO THE SWORD!
HARRALD'S EYESIGHT ISN'T WHAT IT USED TO BE! PUNY . . .?
COME, LET US SEIZE THE BARBARIAN'S WEALTH!
IN FACT! S'FAIR TO SAY HE'S AS BLIND AS A BAT!
. . . AND COME, LET US CARRY OFF THEIR WOMEN!
ME FIRST! ME FIRST!
THOSE ARE THE WOMEN??
THAT WAS A NARROW ESCAPE!
GOOD! HE'S OPENED HIS EYES AT LAST!
WAIT FOR US!!

THAT WAS WORRYING! DID YOU SEE THE ONE WITH THE SHAVING BRUSH NOSE HAIRS? . . . SHE KEPT LOOKING AT ME!!
WHAT NOW? ROGER OF SHERWOOD, EH?
AAH, THIS LOOKS BETTER! I BET I WAS A REAL HERO IN THE GREEN WOOD! . . . "ONCE UPON YE TYME . . ."
ROGER OF SHERWOOD
WHAT ARE TODAY'S PLANS, ROBIN?
TODAY, MEN, WE ATTACK THE SHERIFF OF NOTTINGHAM IN HIS CASTLE — MANY LIVES WILL BE LOST!
LIVES LOST? NOT MINE, NO WAY! I ONLY JOINED UP FOR THE SINGING AND THE WINE . . . TIME TO DODGE OUTA SIGHT!
GOOD TUCK, YOU LOOK FATTER THAN EVER! WHAT AILS THEE?
I DON'T KNOW, GOOD HOOD! I ONLY HAD TWO OF KING JOHN'S DEER FOR SUPPER!
FATTY NOTTINGHAM FOOD! GO ON YE CAMBRIDGE DIET!

GADZOOKIES! IT WASN'T MY GUT AT ALL, JUST SIR ROGER DE COWARDLY HIDING 'NEATH MY DIRTY HABIT!
DODGING BATTLE AGAIN, SIR ROG?
OOH! I'VE GOT A SWORD WOUND ALREADY!
OKAY, OKAY! I'M GOING, I'M GOING! NO NEED TO PUSH!
. . . WITH HIS BAND OF MEN . . . FEARED BY THE BAD, LOVED BY THE GOOD, ROBIN HOOD, ROBIN HOOD, ROBIN HOOOOOD!
LITTLE JOHN IS A MIGHTY WARRIOR THEY TELL ME! I SHOULD BE SAFE IF I STICK TO HIM IN THE BATTLE AGAINST THE WICKED SHERIFF!
YOU'RE LITTLE JOHN??
WHO WERE YOU EXPECTING SIR ROG? A BIG LAD? . . . LET ME DEMONSTRATE MY FIGHTING PROWESS!
JAB

JOIN MY STAFF! AND . . .
. . . YOU CAN LEAD THE FIGHT! UP WITH SIR ROGER! H'ROO! H'ROO!
I NEED A DODGE NOW LIKE I NEVER NEEDED ONE BEFORE! A GOOD DODGE . . . AND FAST! AH, HERE WE ARE . . . "WHEN IN DANGER, REMAIN COMPOSED." COMPOSED, RIGHT, GOTCHA . . . "AND THEN LOOK OUT FOR . . ."
SPLAT!
TOO LATE! AAARGH!

I DON'T NEED A DODGE NOW! IT'S A *MIRACLE* I NEED! WAAA! A *MIRACLE* . . .!!
A MIRACLE!! A ROPE!! SAVED!!
IT'S A FAIR MAID'S GOLDEN LOCKS!
SAVE ME, KIND SIR ROG! I AM THINE!
HEY, MY LUCK'S CHANGED! UP GOES SIR ROG FOR A LITTLE SLAP AN' . . .
GOOD SIR! HELP THE FAIR EDWIGA! I AM TRAPPED HERE THESE FOUR AND FORTY YEARS AND NE'ER A PAIR OF SCISSORS TO TRIM MY GOLDEN NOSE HAIRS . . .

ALLOW ME!
SNIP.
THANK THEE, SIRE!
— AND I THOUGHT SCOTTISH MORAG WAS UGLY!! I'LL TAKE MY CHANCES WITH THE CROCODILES!
KISSY! KISSY!
SHERIFF OF NOTTS, YOU ARE A CHEAT! WE DON'T HAVE SIX-SHOOTERS IN THIS CENTURY!
YOU, ROBIN HOOD, HAS UNDERESTIMATED THE *SHERIFF* OF NOTTINGHAM! YO'R DAYS IS NUMBERED!
SPIN
SPIN
TAKE YO'R LAST LI'L OL' LOOKSEE AT THE BLOOOO SKIES! . . 'COS NOW YO DIES, PARDNER! . . .

CRASH!
SIR ROGER DE COWARDLY IS OUR HERO! HURRAH!
GASP! LOOK! IT . . IT'S . . . IT'S . . .
. . . KING SEAN THE LIONHEART! OUR KING!
BOOM!
BOOM!
BOOM!
007
GOOD KNIGHT, YOU ARE NOW SIR SIR ROGER DE . . .
TIME TO DODGE OFF! KNIGHT-KNIGHT!
OOPS! SORRY!
CRUNCH!

NOW, THOSE WERE EXCITING DODGY TIMES!
HAVE YOU NOT GOT THOSE BOOKS CLEARED UP YET, YOU USELESS DODGER!
YOUR DAD'S TOO SOFT ON YER! GET IT DONE BEFORE I WHACK YER BACKSIDE! Y'HEAR? NO DODGIN' OR YOU'RE HISTORY!
WHACK!
BUT I AM HISTORY!

GAH! IT'S IMPOSSIBLE TO DODGE YOUR DREAMS! THANK GOODNESS IT'S MATHS CLASS TOMORROW!
I CAN'T BELIEVE I HEARD THAT! IT MUST BE A BAD DREAM!

Comic Capers

ZOB

Zob
BANK

Last
Laugh

Comic Capers
THE BEANO books
geddes & grosset